Sher LOCK Homles
CH, Storybook novel

Reading - Difficult words
own Mind
_____ ??

Complete
it!!

Sherlock Holmes was
written on _____

Aditi
mary

Moral of the novel _____

5 Minute Tales

OM
KIDZ

An imprint of Om Books International

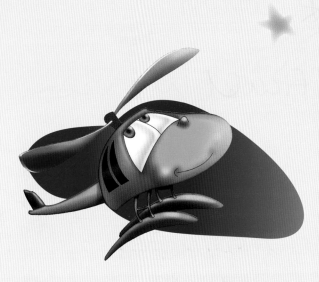

Reprinted in 2014

Published by

OM
KIDZ

An imprint of Om Books International

Corporate & Editorial Office
A 12, Sector 64, Noida 201 301
Uttar Pradesh, India
Phone: +91 120 477 4100
Email: editorial@ombooks.com
Website: www.ombooksinternational.com

Sales Office
4379/4B, Prakash House, Ansari Road
Darya Ganj, New Delhi 110 002, India
Phone: +91 11 2326 3363, 2326 5303
Fax: +91 11 2327 8091
Email: sales@ombooks.com
Website: www.ombooks.com

ISBN : 978-93-81607-46-6

Printed at EIH Press, Gurgaon, India

10 9 8 7 6 5 4 3 2

contents

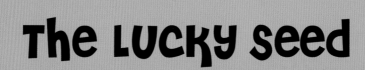

The LUCKY seed

A farmer was on his way to the market to sell a bag of seeds. His cart bumped into a stone and a seed fell out of the bag. "I wish I could be safe underground," thought the seed. A passing buffalo pushed the seed into the ground! "I am so thirsty. I need some water to help me grow," thought the seed. It began to rain!

The next day, the seed had a green shoot. The sun came out and the shoot grew taller. Then a leaf appeared. A hungry bird tried to pluck and eat the seed but the roots saved it. Many years passed and the seed grew into a plant and then into a fine, strong tree. Now, don't you think that the seed was lucky?

2

how the
toad got
its skin

All the birds in the jungle were very excited about the party in the sky. The animals were upset and jealous, as they could not fly up to the sky. But the toad had thought of a plan to join the sky party.

When the birds were about to leave, the toad sneaked into the vulture's guitar and hid there. The birds arrived for the party and were both surprised and angry to see the toad!

When the party was over, the toad again quietly hopped inside the vulture's guitar. But this time, the vulture felt that his guitar had become heavier and shook it. Down went the toad falling to the earth and broke into pieces. Later, the vulture took pity on the toad and stitched up its body into one piece. Even today, one can see where the toad's body was mended by a thread and needle.

Red Birdie's Party

Red Birdie had just moved to Bird Land. He thought, "I shall invite everyone to a party. I will be able to make new friends then." So he flew up and down the street and dropped an envelope in every letterbox of Bird Land. Next morning, he decorated his house and baked a delicious cake and made cheese sandwiches. He waited for his guests to arrive but no one came. He flew outside and saw many birds flying up and down the street with presents in their hands.

"Do you know Red Birdie's house?" they asked him anxiously. Red Birdie laughed when he realised that he had put the numbers on his gate upside-down. His house number was 61 but the numbers on the gate said 91. Everyone had a good laugh. They had lots of fun and Red Birdie made many friends.

4

mitty's wait

Mitty the puppy was bored. Milly the cat was in no mood to play. "Milly, please come out and play with me in the sun!" pleaded Mitty. "Not today, Mitty. I can't. I will just stay in this basket for a while. One of these days, I am going to give you a surprise but you must be patient for now."

Mitty wandered alone for a few days. He would follow his mistress, while she cooked and cleaned. Finally, one day, he saw Milly lying in her basket with FIVE tiny kittens! One white, two black, one grey and one with patches! Milly said, "Mitty, you have been so patient all these days. As a reward, I want you to name my five kittens!" Mitty was so happy and he sat there thinking for a while. Guess what the names were? Rolley, Polley, Dipsey, Doodle and Noodle!

BUNNY RABBIT RUNS A RACE

One day, Bunny Rabbit asked his mother, "Mama, why did my great-great-great-grandfather lose the race against the tortoise? You know, everyone laughed at me when the teacher told us the story." "Great-great-great-grandfather was very proud. That's why he lost the race," said Mama Rabbit.

"But I'll race with Dozy Tortoise and defeat him. I'll show him that only speed and swiftness win races." "No!" said Mama Rabbit, but Bunny did not listen. He went straight to Dozy and said, "Dozy, I challenge you to a race tomorrow. We'll start from here and finish the race at the bridge."

The next morning, the race began. Slimy Frog was the umpire. But lo! To everyone's great wonder, once again, Dozy Tortoise was the winner! He had put on roller skates!

6 TWO Bad mice

Tom Thumb and his wife, Hunca Munka, were two bad mice. They nibbled away at food in the kitchen and littered the place. One night, they both saw something unique. It was a doll's house and had little tables, chairs, beds, and also a table with food. The two tip-toed into the house and discovered that it was a lot of fun.

"The bed fits our size," said Hunca Munka. "But we must finish the food first," explained Tom anxiously. But lo! When they bit the ham, it hurt. They tried the bread too but Tom's tooth almost broke. The two bad mice were very disappointed as the food was not real. The two walked back sadly to their hole. What terrible luck for them!

mrs. Tittlemouse and the Bumblebee

7

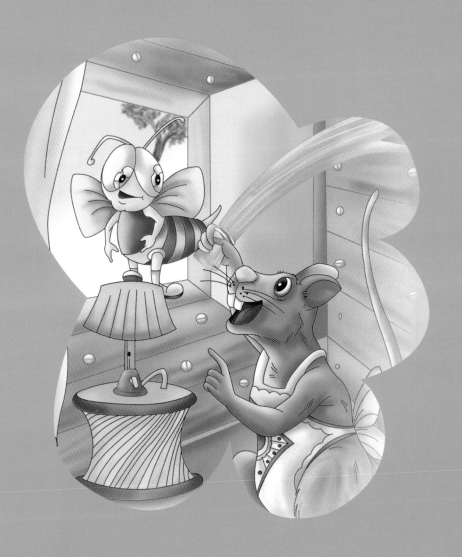

Mrs. Tittlemouse baked delicious cakes everyday. A bumblebee who lived nearby wanted some, but Mrs. Tittlemouse disliked insects. If she ever spotted a spider weaving a web, she chased the spider out of her house with her broomstick. "How will I ever get to taste those those delicious cakes?" wondered the bumblebee.

One day, a caterpillar happened to sit on the window sill. "How dare you come here!" shouted Mrs. Tittlemouse. "I have hurt my leg!" said the caterpillar. The bumblebee saw Mrs. Tittlemouse gently apply medicines to the caterpillar's wounds and then also offer it some cake.

So, the next morning, the bumblebee buzzed near the window, complaining of a headache. Alas! Mrs. Tittlemouse saw through his plan and chased him away!

The stream

It was a hot summer day. Little Billy felt thirsty and worn out. He stopped for a while and saw a clear stream flowing. "The water is cold and my body is hot. Mamma said that it's not good to drink water when you are out in the sun," thought Billy. "What do I care," came the second thought. He drank the icy cold water. Suddenly, Billy felt weak and fainted the next moment.

When his eyes opened, he found himself in bed with high fever. "The water of the stream was really bad," said Billy. "No, Billy, you are wrong. This happens when kids do not listen to their parents," replied his mother. Billy felt very sorry, so his mother gave him a hug and took him to a duck pond when he was well again.

The Arab
and his Camel

It was a cold winter night. An Arab was resting in his tent when his camel peeped inside and asked, "Master, it's very cold outside. Please allow me to put my head inside your warm tent."

The kind master took pity on the poor animal and agreed to the camel's request. A little later, the camel asked, "Master, please let me put my neck inside your tent as well." Once again the master allowed him to do so.

Next, the camel asked if he could put his forelegs in and again the kind master agreed. Very soon, the camel was completely inside the tent. But the tent was too small for both the master and the camel.

Finally, the camel asked his master to leave the tent so that he could be more comfortable. By now the master was very angry and turned the camel out in the cold again.

monster under my bed!

Little Kate tucked herself into bed and was about to drift into sleep when she heard a loud noise. THUMP! THUMP! Kate was petrified and she called out to her grandmother, "Grandma! There is a monster under my bed!" "That is just your naughty little heart, dearie," said Grandma.

Kate tried to go back to sleep and just then, she heard THUMP! THUMP! SCRITCH! SCRITCH! "Grandma!" she cried. "The monster is scratching his claws on the floor! Please save me!" "There is no monster, Katie!" said Grandma. "It is just your toes rubbing on the quilt!" When Katie tried to sleep once again, she felt something wet on her face! With a lot of courage, she opened her eyes to see the monster. "Grandma!" cried out Katie, "this is no monster! It's a sweet little puppy!" Katie and the puppy snuggled and slept soundly.

The Four wives

A rich merchant had four wives. He showered his first wife with valuable gifts for she was very beautiful. His second wife belonged to a very rich family, so he took her along to meet kings and famous people. His third wife was very educated and she often gave him advice on his business. However, he neglected his fourth wife who was neither beautiful nor very educated. But she was a kind human being.

Misfortune struck the merchant and he lost all his property and became a pauper. The first three wives immediately deserted him. Only the fourth wife remained with him. Now the merchant realised his mistake. He said to his fourth wife, "I was a foolish man and didn't know that after all a good heart matters more than looks, wealth or education!"

12

The Kites and the swans

In olden times, kites and swans were blessed with an amazing talent. They could sing very well and used to entertain everyone, young and old, with their melodious voice. Sometimes they would even sing in the king's court. People came from far and wide to hear them sing.

One day, they heard the neigh of a horse. They were delighted by this unfamiliar sound. They thought the horse's neigh was better than their voice and wished that they could also neigh like the horse. So, they tried very hard to imitate that sound. As a result they forgot what they knew best—to sing. No one came to hear them anymore and praise their beautiful songs. In the desire to learn something that was not fit for them, they lost what they already had.

13

Billy Learns to Fly

One day, Billy asked his mother, "Mom, may I go outside?" "Be careful, it's very windy today," said his mother. Billy ran out excitedly. Leaves flew in all directions and chased each other outside.

"How I wish I was also a leaf and was as free as them," said Billy. Suddenly, a maple leaf touched Billy's side and he found himself lifted up with the leaf. "I can fly, I can fly," exclaimed Billy, as they swirled round and round. Billy was thoroughly enjoying himself. "This is so much fun," he cried. Suddenly, Billy heard his mom shout, "Billy, get up! You'll be late for school." Billy opened his eyes and realised that he had been dreaming all along. "Maybe I'll fly some other day," he thought and ran to get ready for school.

gabby
TURNS BIUE

Gabby, the little duckling, was very naughty. One day, Gabby sneaked out to go and play in the pond. He looked up at the sky and thought, "The sky is so blue. I must fly in the fluffy clouds." He dived in the air, did a little jig and a somersault. "Wow...the clouds are so soft!" said he as they tickled him while he flew.

Soon, it was dark but Gabby couldn't find his way back home. He flew and flew until he lost all his strength and fell down into a big cauldron containing a strange blue liquid. When Gabby finally returned home, his friends were stunned to see Gabby. His body had turned blue and his beak was white. Poor Gabby! No matter how much he washed himself in the pond, the colour didn't go and he is still blue.

15

Arnie's Caterpillar

One afternoon, when Arnie was flying a kite, he felt something crawl on his left foot. It was a small caterpillar, and just as he was about to shake it off, a faint voice called out, "Arnie, Arnie." The caterpillar was actually trying to talk to him! The tiny caterpillar said, "Please don't be rude to me, Arnie." So, he picked up the little caterpillar and put him on his palm. "Oh, thank you! All my friends have turned into beautiful butterflies and gone away. Will you be my friend, Arnie?" said the caterpillar.

Arnie felt sorry for the lonely caterpillar and agreed to be his friend. He kept the caterpillar in a glass jar in his room until he became a butterfly and they both played in the meadow.

The Truthful Dove

Once, on a stormy night, a dove and a bat asked an owl for shelter. The owl lived in a hollow tree and unwillingly let the two animals enter his house. He was quite selfish and vain and did not like to share his food with anyone either. The bat was very sly. He knew that if he praised the owl, the owl would be happy and he would get a good share of the food in return.

So the bat flattered the owl and the owl was very pleased. He said "Here my dear friend, help yourself to more food." But the dove did not like to flatter others and remained silent. The owl loved flattery and was angry at the dove for keeping quiet. He threw the dove out of the house. By now, the storm was almost over and the dove flew away to meet her family.

17

the king and his hawk

Once, a king was crossing a desert, his pet hawk perched on his shoulders. The hot sun made him thirsty and he went to look for a stream. Luckily, he chanced upon a fountain not very far. He knelt down and was about to drink the water, when suddenly the hawk swooped down and pecked his hand. He stooped down to drink the water again. But the hawk pecked his hand again.

The thirsty king screamed angrily at the hawk. When he stooped down, something glistened in the water. It was a fierce poisonous snake. The king knew that a single sip of that water would have killed him. He felt terrible for screaming and apologized to the hawk, petting it lovingly. The hawk too, forgave his master.

The mouse, the Bird and the sausage

A bird, a mouse and a sausage lived together. The bird was in charge of getting wood from the forest every day, the mouse had to get water and make the fire and the sausage was in charge of cooking.

They lived happily until one day, the bird met another bird who told him that his work was the most difficult while his other friends had easy jobs. Now, the bird refused to go to the forest the next day and demanded that they should exchange their work. The mouse and the sausage were against this proposal but were forced to agree to the bird's wish.

Alas! Everything went wrong. When the sausage went to cut wood, it slipped down from the tree and was eaten up by a dog, the mouse burned itself and perished while cooking and the bird fell into the well!

19 mr. Toby Regains his Life

Mr. Toby was a handsome, rich cat. After all, he was Mrs. Wilson's pet. He was reading a letter which was from Miss Chloe, the most beautiful cat. "Toby! I am dying for your love. Will you marry me?" Chloe had written. Toby couldn't believe his eyes. He received many love letters now and then. But to know that Chloe was madly in love with him was very good news.

He began dancing on the wooden roof in excitement. He hopped and jumped so happily that quite expectedly, he tripped and fell off the roof and died. The entire cat community joined the funeral procession with Mrs. Wilson and Miss Chloe. As the procession passed the market square, the smell of fish stirred Mr. Toby from his death-sleep. "M-e-o-w," yawned Toby and opened his eyes. And "MEOW" cheered all, happily.

The Lonely Deer

Once, on a tiny island near the sea, there lived a young deer, all by himself. He was very lonely as there was no one to play with him. He did not even know how to get out of the island.

One day, a fish took pity on him and told the lonely deer to follow him to the big forest where there were many deer. The deer tried hard to swim but could not. Next day, a swan tried to teach the deer how to fly but the deer soon gave up.

Sometime later, a big elephant passed by the island. "Come, climb on to my back, little deer. I'll take you to the big forest," said the elephant loudly. He bent down and the deer hopped onto his back. "Wow! I'll never be lonely again," cried the deer in joy. Soon, the elephant and the deer became the very best of friends.

21

hoo-hoo's party

One day, Hoo-Hoo owl thought, "I will throw a party at midnight and invite, Taylor the mouse, Soft-Ears the rabbit, Singer the nightingale and Frisky the squirrel. And that will be a delicious meal indeed!"

"A grand party!" squeaked the mouse in delight. "And so much to eat!" said Singer when they heard about the party. "But why should the party begin at midnight?" thought Frisky, after reading the owl's invitation card very carefully.

So at night, instead of going inside Hoo-Hoo's house, they all watched from a distance. Inside, a group of owls joked, "Today is the grand feast!" When they heard this, Frisky and the other realized they were going to be the food themselves, and ran away!

mr. maggs and monty

Mr. Maggs had a dog named Monty, who loved to go for long walks. Monty had long legs and walked so fast that Mr. Maggs had to run to keep pace with his dog. He had to tightly hold on to his scarf and hat, so that they would not fall off while he ran.

One evening, Mr. Maggs went to the market leaving Monty at home. When he returned, Monty saw that his master had a huge parcel in his hand, "What could this be?" thought Monty curiously. Next morning, Monty leapt out and ran fast as usual, but Mr. Maggs was surprisingly right behind his dog, whizzing along! So, Monty stopped and looked around. And guess what he saw? Mr. Maggs was wearing roller skates! "So that's what was in the mysterious parcel?" thought Monty and happily ran again.

The salt merchant

Once, a peddler was going home with his ass after buying salt. His house was across the stream. When they reached the stream, the ass accidentally fell into the water. When he got up, his load had been reduced since the salt had dissolved in the water. This delighted the ass. Next time the peddler again loaded him with salt and this time the ass fell down on purpose. He got up again feeling his load lightened and brayed in triumph.

The peddler understood the ass's trick and decided to teach him a lesson. This time he loaded the ass with sponges instead of salt. So when the ass purposely fell down into the stream, he felt that his load had doubled as the sponges had become laden with water. Thus the ass's trick backfired on him.

24

hermia
the hippo

Hermia the hippo lived in a zoo. One day, Hermia escaped from the zoo and ran away to Mike's house. Mike knew that hippos and boys couldn't stay together, so he hid Hermia in their swimming pool. Hermia stayed in the water quietly and didn't make any noise. She was quite pleased with herself.

At night, Mike sneaked out food from the kitchen and Hermia gulped it all in seconds! Hippos really have a large appetite. But Mother found out about Hermia when they were playing in his room and jumping on the bed. She was shocked at the sight. "Mike! You know that hippos stay in zoos! We must take her back immediately," cried Mother. Now Mike goes to the zoo every Sunday to meet Hermia.

The gardener and the good king

There was a gardener who tended his garden passionately. He loved all his vegetables and flowers. His vegetables were very tasty and famous throughout the kingdom. His garden was a delight for onlookers. One day, a hare broke into his garden and damaged the plants and the vegetables. The gardener tried to chase it away but every day the hare would plunder his garden.

At last, the gardener went to the king for help. The king sent his army to the garden. There was a feast before the search for the hare began. The hare was found at last but the king's hunters had done more damage to the garden than a hundred hares could have done. And the poor gardener wept and wondered, "Ah! Will my garden ever be the same again?"

THE BLACK SCHOOL

The Black School was run by the Devil. Here, students were taught witchcraft and ancient magic. The school was located in a dark dungeon below the Earth. The Devil had a strange custom—he would keep back a boy with him from the graduating batch of students as his assistant. On the last day of school every year, as soon as the last bell chimed and the boys ran, the Devil always managed to pull one student back.

This year as the bell rang, the children sprang up from their seats and rushed towards the stairs. Tom was a slow runner and the Devil knew this. But Tom was smart too. He wore a very loose cloak and as soon as the Devil grabbed it, the cloak came off and Tom ran away from the school!

27

The First messenger

Flurry was a little girl. She lived in a big house which was surrounded by many trees. One bright morning, Flurry woke up and decided to go for a walk. Suddenly, she heard a soft whistle. She looked around but saw nothing. The whistle sounded again. This time, Flurry leapt with joy. It was a Bluebird!

"Where have you come from Bluebird," she asked curiously. "I was spending time in warm Australia. But now that spring's here again, I am back," explained the little bird. "And why do you whistle?" she asked. "I want to spread the news all over that spring is here!" said the Bluebird and flew off to another tree.

28

THE FLOWERS

"Rose is the most beautiful flower," said little Louisa. "But I think lilies are prettier than roses," replied her sister Caroline. "I simply love its colour." Mary was listening to her younger sisters talking about flowers. She said, "When you are talking of flowers, how can you forget the violet? I think violets are the best."

Their mother heard them talking and said, "My dear, each flower teaches us something. While violet stands for modesty, lily teaches innocence and rose shows love for God and all its creatures." Now Louisa, Caroline and Mary found all the flowers equally beautiful!

29

JUMPER the hare gets a new coat

Jumper Hare was worried. The snow had covered the land where he used to jump and play. "Where will I play and where will I hide?" he thought. In summer, his brown fur was almost the same colour as the brown leaves that covered the ground, so it was difficult to spot him but now that the entire area had turned white, it had become difficult to hide.

One morning, Jumper woke up to find himself covered with snow. He tried to brush his coat. He brushed and brushed and brushed. To his surprise, his fur remained white and he was even more astonished the next day, when he saw that even his tail had turned white. "At last I can hide like before," he said and danced and skipped and hopped in joy.

30

The Proud Frog

A large frog, who was very vain, believed that he was the most handsome frog and wanted to grow even bigger. He often admired his reflection in a pond and swelling with pride would boast to his friends, "Look how big I am!"

One day, an ox was passing by the pond. The proud frog looked at the ox and asked his friends, "Am I as big as the ox?" His friends, who were tired of hearing the proud frog boast about himself every day, said that he wasn't as big as the ox.

The proud frog was furious and wanted to prove his friends wrong. He puffed himself up to become bigger and bigger to show his friends that he could be as big as the ox. He huffed and he puffed and all of a sudden, he burst and that was the end of the vain frog!

31

Audrey's Adventure

It was getting dark, and Audrey had to return home from her aunt's house. She put on her coat and said goodbye. Audrey's house was just a ten minute walk from her aunt's. As she walked, Audrey started humming. There were five days left for her birthday. She was busy thinking about what she would do when suddenly, she bumped into a tree. It was quite dark.

She looked around and didn't know where she was. She had lost her way. "Oh" she wailed, "I don't know where I am." She sat under the tree and started sobbing. Suddenly, she felt a dog licking her face. "Oh Buddy," I am glad you found me. Just then, her father appeared with a torch and picked her up in his arms. "Audrey, you must come home before it's dark!" Audrey wiped her tears and gave her dad a big hug.

32 BARBOLITO'S BAD DAY AT SCHOOL

Barbolito was short and had curly hair. The other boys in his class always jeered at him. One day, his mother saw him crying, "What is the matter, Barbolito?" she asked. "All the boys make fun of me because I look different," explained Barbolito. "They are foolish boys," said his mother, "I will speak to your teacher about this."

The next day, when Barbolito went to school his teacher called him aside and said, "You should not cry because people say mean things. Why don't you talk about all the exciting things you do, like scuba diving and chess. This way the children will get to know you better and will also discover how special you are." Barbolito took his teacher's advise and from that day on, he had many friends.

growing good corn

Farmer Peter won the gold medal for growing the best corn in the village. He became famous when the newspapers wrote about him. One day, a reporter was amazed to find Peter distributing his seeds to other farmers in the village. "If you distribute your seeds, how will you win the competition for growing the best corn next year?" the reporter asked.

"Sir," replied Peter, "the wind picks up pollen from crops and flowers and spreads it everywhere. So if my neighbours do not grow good crops, my field will suffer too. If I need to grow good corn, I must help my neighbours too."

The reporter realised how wise the farmer was. To be happy one must make others happy too.

The Just Punishment

Afarmer owned a fertile piece of land. He was rich but mean. He left his poor parents to fend for themselves. When they approached him for money and food, he refused. The old couple turned sadly away. On their way back, they met a midget who gave them a large chunk of cheese and some herbs to eat. When they ate the herb and the cheese, the skies thundered and a huge storm swept through the town. Instead of their small hut, there stood a huge mansion.

The couple was amazed at this and went at once to share the good news with their son. But they saw his fertile land was no longer there! "The storm swept away everything I had!" he cried. The parents consoled their son and took him home with them.

35

The Death of the Little hen

Once, a little hen and a little cock were eating nuts. A nut got stuck in the hen's throat! The cock rushed to fetch water for her from a well nearby. But the well told him to bring him some red silk from a bride before he could take out any water. The cock went to the bride, who told him to bring her a wreath. The cock finally brought water for the hen. But it was too late.

The hen was already dead! A carriage pulled by six mice was built to carry the hen to the grave. On the way, they reached a stream; a straw, a coal and a stone tried to help them to cross but they all slipped and drowned in the stream. The cock managed to reach the other side and buried the hen. But he was heartbroken without his friend and soon died.

36

Jeremy Fisher

Jeremy Fisher was a frog who loved to fish. One day, Jeremy wore his coat and took his fishing rod, some worms and set off fishing. "Today, I will invite Isaac Newton and Ptolemy Tortoise for a dinner of trout!" he thought and went to the stream. While he sat on his little green leaf boat and rowed with a thin reed, he saw shoals of fish scurrying about.

Jeremy Fisher was delighted. Suddenly, a huge trout passed by and rocked his tiny boat. Jeremy fell overboard and splashed into the water. The trout licked poor Jeremy and tried to gobble him. Somehow, he managed to escape from the huge fish and ran back home! Now Jeremy Fisher did not know what to give his guests for dinner. Isaac Newton got along with him some juicy salads and Ptolemy Tortoise ate weeds. And poor Jeremy Fisher had a butterfly sandwich.

37

Ali and the Sultan

Once, there was a man named Ali. He was very funny and was always making fun of the sultan. Everybody knew about Ali's jokes and the sultan himself, came to know about them. The sultan was very angry and called Ali to the palace. Clever Ali, on reaching the palace, began to sing the sultan's praises. He loudly praised the sultan's looks, wealth, and power.

The pleased ruler then said to Ali, "Wonderful! You have made me very happy! As a reward you can choose one of these beautiful saddles!" When Ali returned with a donkey's saddle on his back, everybody asked him what the sultan had said. Ali winked and replied, "The sultan was so pleased that he gave me one of his own robes to wear!" Everyone burst out laughing.

38

Katie and
her Reflection

Katie was a silly girl. She would often get a beating from her mother for making stupid mistakes but she just never learnt!

One day, she went for a walk in the woods. When she grew tired, she sat down near a lake to eat a sandwich. After that she fell asleep. When she woke up, it was very dark. She could not see her reflection in the water. And silly Katie thought that since she could not see herself, she was lost. Finally, after wandering around for some time, she reached home and knocked on the door and asked, "Is Katie inside?" A voice from inside said, "She must be in her bedroom." Silly Katie thought that if Katie was inside then she must be someone else. So she went away and never returned.

Titles in this Series

ISBN: 978-93-82607-88-5

ISBN: 978-93-82607-76-2

ISBN: 978-93-82607-89-2

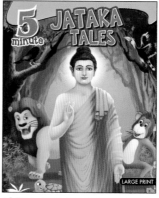

ISBN: 978-93-82607-26-7

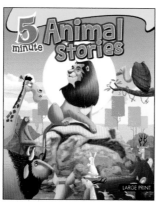

ISBN: 978-93-82607-87-8

ISBN: 978-93-81607-46-6

PARTS OF SPEECH

★ There are nine parts of the speech.

↓ nouns → pronouns → verbs → Prepo-ions

↓ conjunctions / Adjectives articles

adverbs

interjections.

a) NOUNS = Nouns are naming words

28-04-2016   WORD POWER   E-w

[F] [L] [I] [V] [V] [E] [R]

Meaning - An automobile, especial one that is small, inexpensive and old

usage - He held up his thumb ar the very first feivver coming down the road stopped for him.